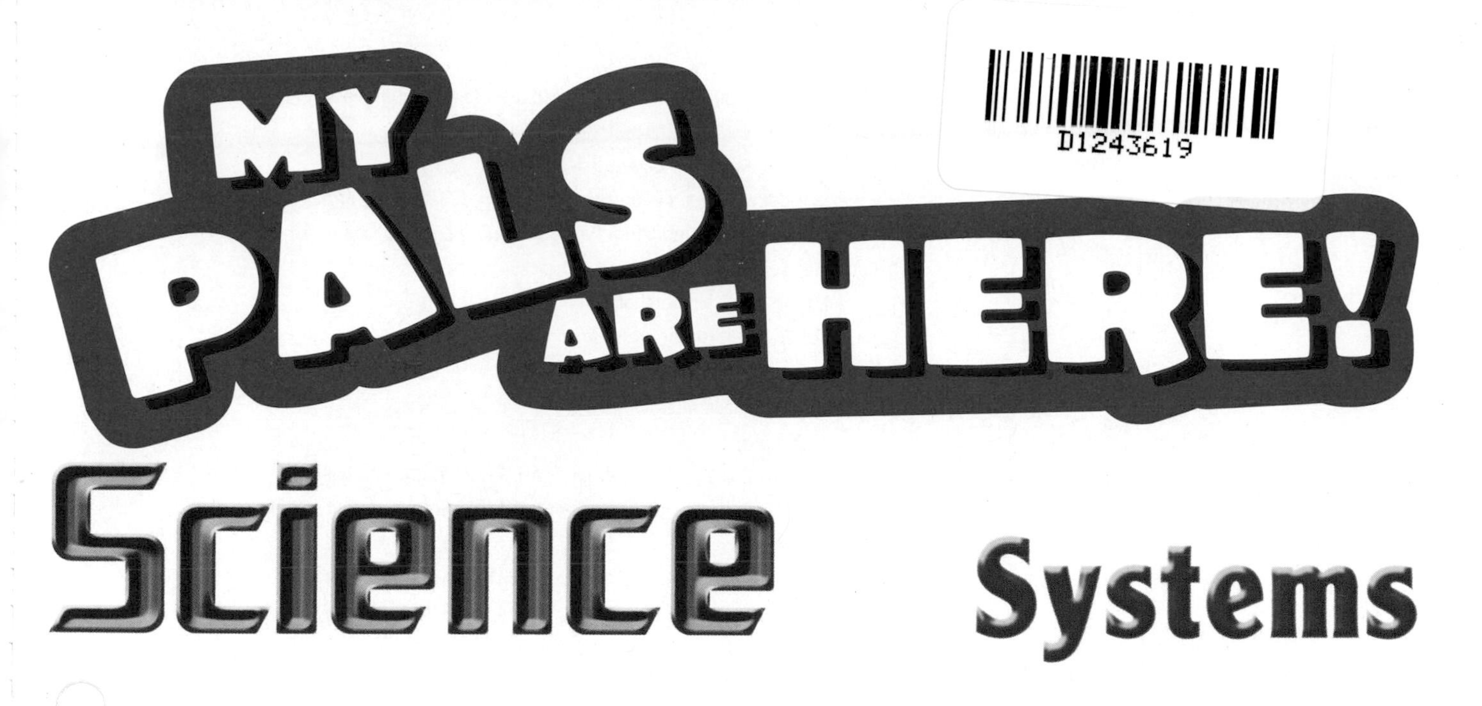

Science

Systems

2nd Edition

Primary 5&6

Activity Book

Koh Siew Luan • Dr Kwa Siew Hwa • Teo-Gwan Wai Lan
Science Education Consultant: Dr Charles Chew

Published by Marshall Cavendish Education
An imprint of Marshall Cavendish International (Singapore) Private Limited
Times Centre, 1 New Industrial Road, Singapore 536196
Customer Service Hotline: (65) 6411 0820
E-mail: tmesales@sg.marshallcavendish.com
Website: www.marshallcavendish.com/education

First edition published
in 2003 as
My Pals are Here! Primary 5A(EM1/2) Science Activity Book
My Pals are Here! Primary 5B(EM1/2) Science Activity Book
in 2004 as
My Pals are Here! Primary 6A(EM1/2) Science Activity Book
My Pals are Here! Primary 6B(EM1/2) Science Activity Book

Second edition 2009
Reprinted 2010, 2011, 2012 (twice)

ISBN 978-981-01-8752-1

Printed in Singapore by Times Printers, www.timesprinters.com

Acknowledgements

The authors and publisher would like to thank the following for permission to reproduce copyright material:

Alexis Rudd: **Page 17** (copepod)

We are also grateful to the following individuals:
- Models and their families
- All those who have kindly loaned us items for the photos featured

While every effort has been made to contact the copyright holders of the materials reproduced, we have been unsuccessful in some instances. To these copyright holders, we offer our sincere apologies and hope that they will take our liberty in good faith. We welcome any information that would enable us to contact the copyright holders/owners concerned.

Preface

MY PALS ARE HERE! Primary 5&6 Science brings pupils on an exciting and meaningful journey of Science learning!

Features that build knowledge and understanding

Features that extend knowledge

Features that help revision

To highlight safety tips and teacher guidance

Contents

Name: ______________________ Class: __________ Date: __________

Activity 1.1 In the flow

Process skills

Identifying : the distribution of water throughout the plant
Comparing : the movement of water in two halves of a celery stalk

Aim: To show the movement of water in a plant through the water-carrying tubes

Materials: A stalk of celery, blue and red food colouring, two 1000 mℓ beakers, knife

Procedures

1. Cut part of a stalk of celery into two halves, as shown in the diagram below.
2. Fill two beakers with 500 mℓ of water each.
3. Mix two tablespoons of red food colouring in one beaker and two tablespoons of blue food colouring into the other beaker of water.
4. Place one half of the stalk of celery in the blue-coloured water and the other half in the red-coloured water as shown in the diagram below.

Handle the food colouring with care. Do not stain your uniform.

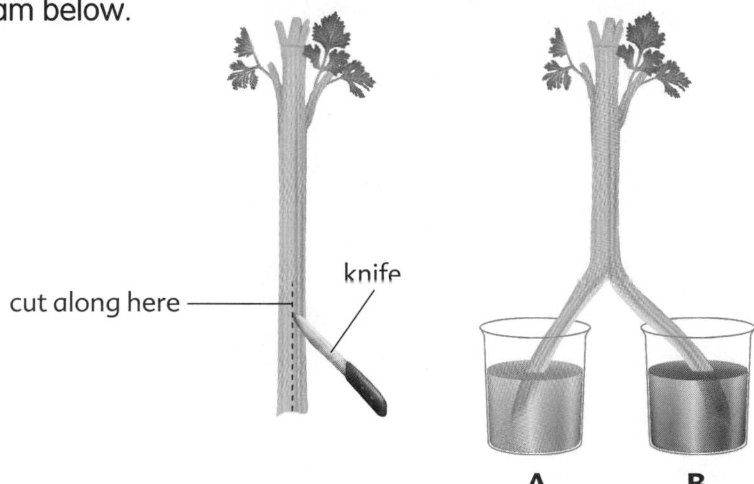

5. Leave the set-up aside overnight.
6. Observe the stem and leaves of the stalk of celery the next day.

Observations

1. Cut a cross-section of the stalk of celery from parts A and B. Draw the cross-section in the space below and colour the stained spots.

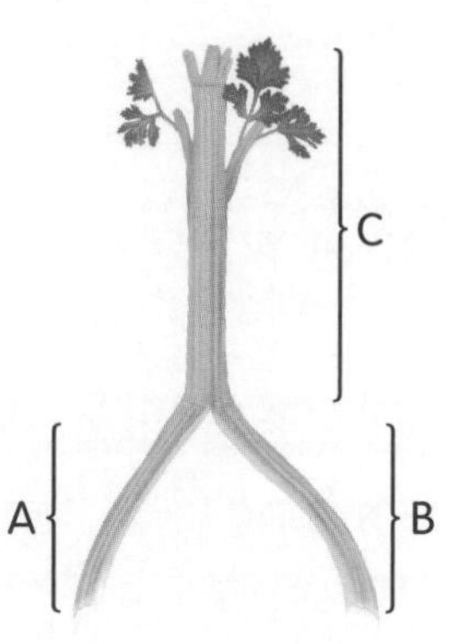

A

B

2. Take sections from part C and observe the stains. Is there any mixing of the blue and red colours in any part of this upper portion of the stalk? Explain your answer.

___

___

Conclusion

In the diagram below, draw the tubes that run up the stem transporting water to the whole plant.

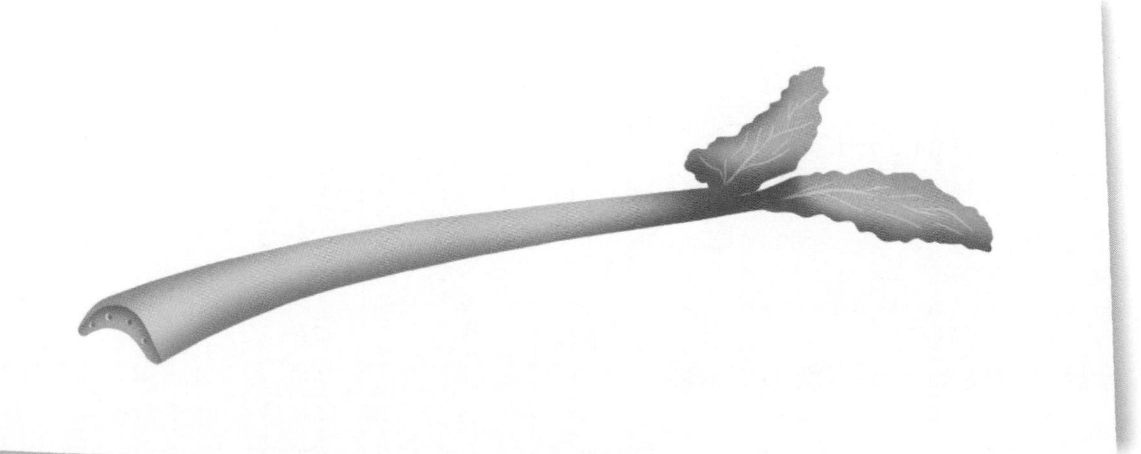

Question

Compare the stem-sections from the base with one near the top. What difference do you notice about the way they are coloured? Why is this so?

____

____

____

Extension

1. How do you think you can obtain a carnation that is half red and half blue?

   ____

   ____

   ____

2. Florists usually cut stems at an angle as shown on the right. Why?

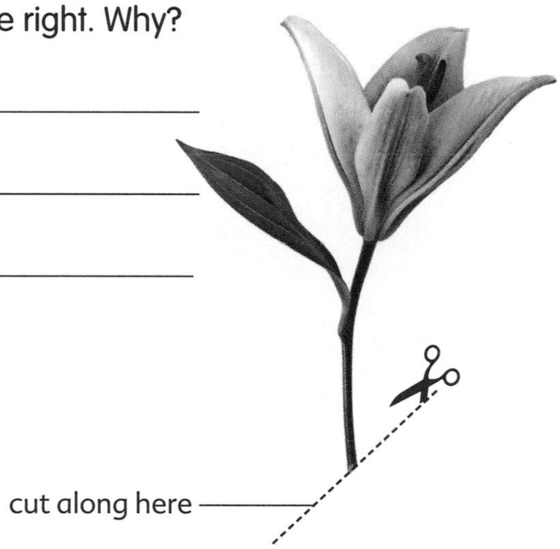

   ____

   ____

   ____

cut along here

Name: ______________________ Class: __________ Date: __________

Activity 1.2 Sugar in the flow

Process skill

Inferring : the substances carried in the tubes

Aim: To show the movement of food in the plants

Joe is investigating what happens when a ring of food-carrying tubes is removed from a sunflower plant. He cuts off a portion of the stem of a sunflower plant as shown below.

He leaves the plant aside for a week. This is what he observes at the end of the week.

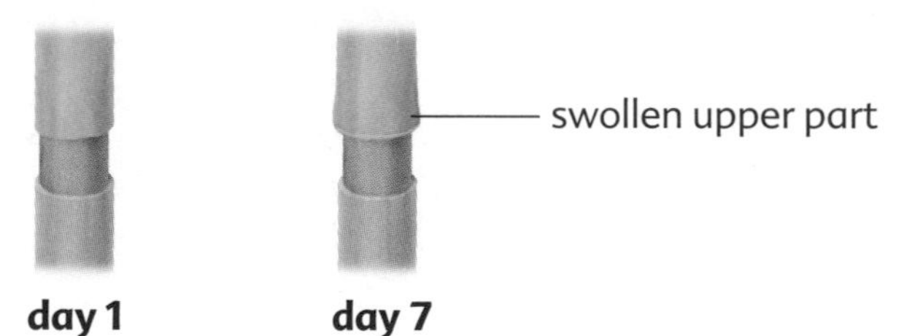

Questions

1. Is it still possible for water to be transported from the roots to the other parts of the plant? Explain your answer.

____

____

2. Why does the upper part of the cut region swell?

____

____

Name: ______________________ Class: __________ Date: __________

Activity 2.1 The lung machine

Process skills

Observing : the model set-up
Inferring : how your respiratory system works

Teacher Demonstration

Aim: To set up a lung model and understand how our lungs work when we breathe

Materials: A transparent plastic cup, a straw, two balloons, plasticine, measuring tape

Your teacher will show you how to make a lung model like the one shown below.

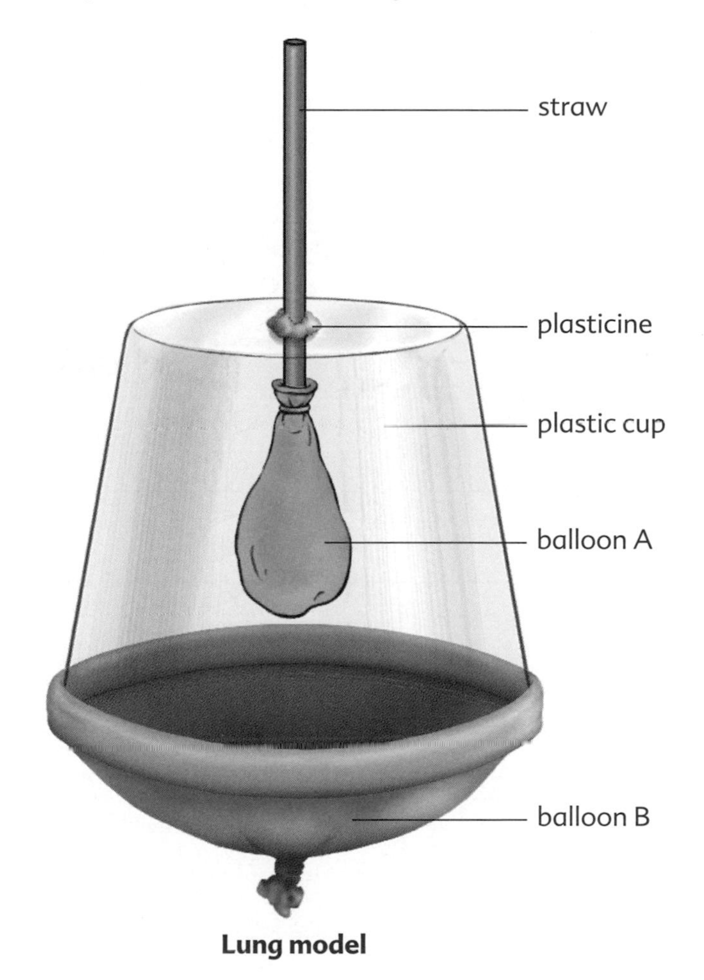

Lung model

Procedures

1. Place a hand between your abdomen and chest.
2. Breathe in and out. Observe what happens to your abdomen and chest.
3. Get your friend to measure your chest size using a measuring tape when you:

   (a) breathe in : __________ cm

   (b) breathe out : __________ cm

4. Now, gently pull down balloon B. Observe and state what happens to balloon A.

   ____

5. Next, slowly release balloon B. Observe and state what happens to balloon A again.

   ____

Questions

1. Which parts of your body are like the following parts of the lung model?

Lung model	Your body
Straw	
Balloon A	

2. (a) Using a pencil, draw the missing parts of the human respiratory system. Label all the parts of the respiratory system (including those that you have drawn).

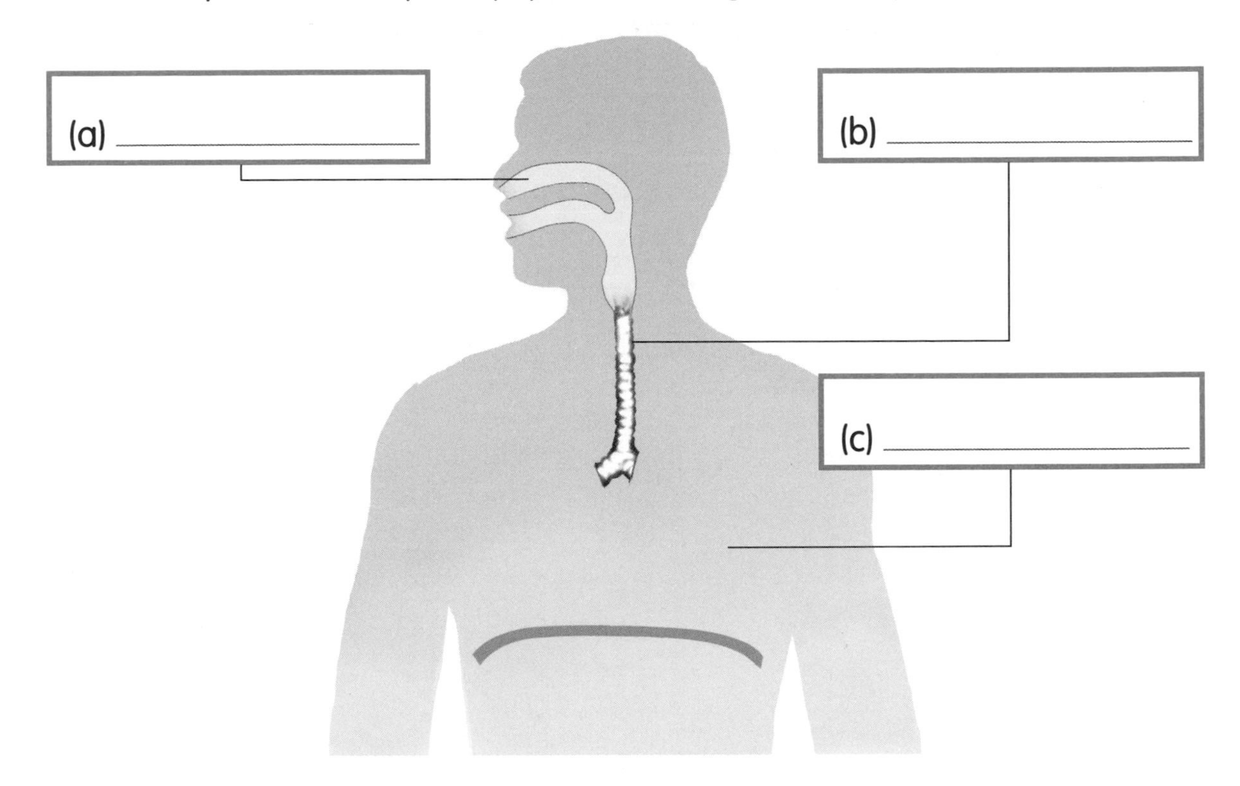

(b) In the diagram above, use arrows (⟶) to show how air enters your respiratory system.

(c) Then use broken arrows (- - >) to show how air leaves your respiratory system.

Reinforcement

Compare the lung model and the human respiratory system.

	Lung model	Human respiratory system
Similarity		
Difference		

Name: ______________________ Class: __________ Date: __________

Activity 2.2 I'll huff and I'll puff

Process skill

Observing : how the amount of air we breathe can be measured

Teacher Demonstration

Aim: To find out the volume of air that can be taken in and out during normal breathing

Materials: A 100 mℓ beaker, a 1.5 ℓ (1500 mℓ) plastic bottle with a cap, a permanent marker, a trough, 50 cm long rubber tube

Procedures

1. Measure 50 mℓ of water in a beaker. Pour the water into a 1.5 ℓ plastic bottle. Mark the level of water with a permanent marker.
2. Repeat step 1 until you have filled the bottle with 1.5 ℓ of water. Make sure that the bottle is filled to its brim with water. Screw on the bottle cap.
3. Fill the trough with water until it is half-full.
4. Invert the bottle and submerge the mouth of the bottle in the trough of water. Then, unscrew the bottle cap slowly. Keep the mouth of the bottle submerged in the water at all times.
5. Thread a 50 cm long rubber tube into the bottle as shown on the right.

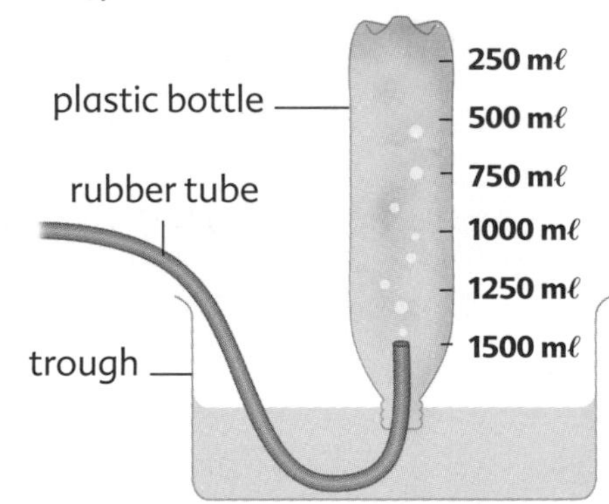

6. Take a deep breath and blow out as much air as you can into the rubber tube.
7. Look at the markings on the bottle and find out the volume of air you have exhaled into the bottle. The volume of air in the bottle represents the volume of air that can be breathed in or out during normal breathing.

   $1\ \ell = 1000\ cm^3$

   The volume of air in the bottle is ______________ cm^3.

Do not place the tube into your mouth immediately after your classmate has finished blowing into it. Wipe the free end of the tube with alcohol or water before you blow into it.

Name: ____________________ Class: __________ Date: __________

Activity 2.3 Fishy business

Process skill

Observing : the gills of a fish

Teacher Demonstration

Aim: To study the respiratory system of a fish

Materials: A small fish (for example, an ikan kuning), a hand lens, a big bowl of crushed ice

Procedures

1. Place a fish on a bowl of crushed ice for five minutes.
2. Pull back the gill cover.

Pull back the gill cover gently to prevent water from splashing onto you. If your clothes get stained, wash them immediately.

Observations

3. Use a hand lens to observe what is below the gill cover.
4. Draw what you see in the box below. Label your drawing.

Questions

1. (a) What is the colour of the gills?

   ____

   (b) Why do you think the gills are this colour?

   ____

   ____

2. How are the gills you have drawn useful to the fish?

   ____

   ____

   ____

Conclusion

Fish do not have ______________ like mammals. They breathe through their

______________ . These are found on the sides of their ______________ .

Oxygen from the water that passes through the gills, is taken in by the

______________ .

Name: ____________________ Class: __________ Date: __________

Activity 3.1 Go with the flow

Process skill

Elaborating : our circulatory system

Aim: To describe the movement of blood in the human circulatory system

Study the simplified circulatory system shown below and identify **A** to **D**.

upper body parts
(e.g. head, neck and arms)

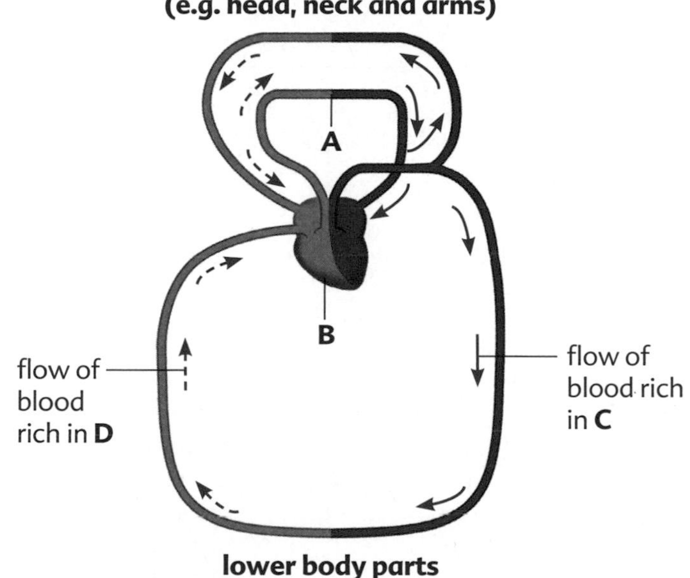

lower body parts
(e.g. stomach, intestines, legs)

A: ___ ___ ___ ___ S

B: ___ ___ A ___ ___

C: ___ ___ ___ G ___ ___

D: ___ ___ R ___ ___ ___

___ ___ O ___ ___ ___ ___

Complete the following sentences.

The body has about 5 litres of blood travelling through its

[ ][ ][ ][ ][ ][ ][ ][ ][ ][ ][ ] system. The

[ ][ ][ ][ ][ ], the [ ][ ][ ][ ][ ], and the

[ ][ ][ ][ ][ ] vessels work together with the lungs. The pumping of the heart forces the blood through the system.

Name: ______________________ Class: __________ Date: __________

Activity 3.2 Run for your life!

Process skill

Observing : the pulse rate of an individual

Aim: To learn how to make and use a pulse detector

Materials: Plasticine, toothpick

Procedures

1. Flatten a small piece of plasticine and stick a toothpick in the middle. You have just made a pulse detector.

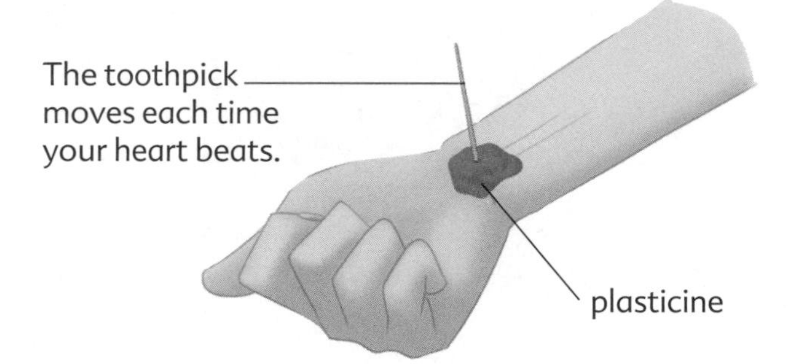

2. Balance the plasticine on your wrist, where you can feel your pulse. Can you see the toothpick move?

3. Count the number of times the toothpick moves in one minute. Record your pulse rate. Your pulse rate is the number of times your heart beats in a minute. This is the resting heart rate. The resting heart rate is the minimum number of beats required by the heart to maintain body functions at rest.

4. Walk quickly for five minutes. Stop and balance the pulse detector on your wrist again. Record your pulse rate.

5. Run on the spot for five minutes. Stop, measure and record your pulse rate again.

Observations

Action	Pulse rate (beats per minute)
Resting rate	
After walking quickly for five minutes	
After running for five minutes	

Conclusion

The pulse rate is the ____________________ (number of beats/volume of blood) your heart beats in a minute. Your pulse rate ____________________ (is independent of/varies with) the type of activity you do.

Extension

The resting heart rate of four individuals are presented in the table below.

	Heart rate (beats per minute)
5 year-old child	88
10 year-old child	86
25 year-old adult	78
55 year-old adult	64

(a) Plot a line graph to present the data presented in the table.

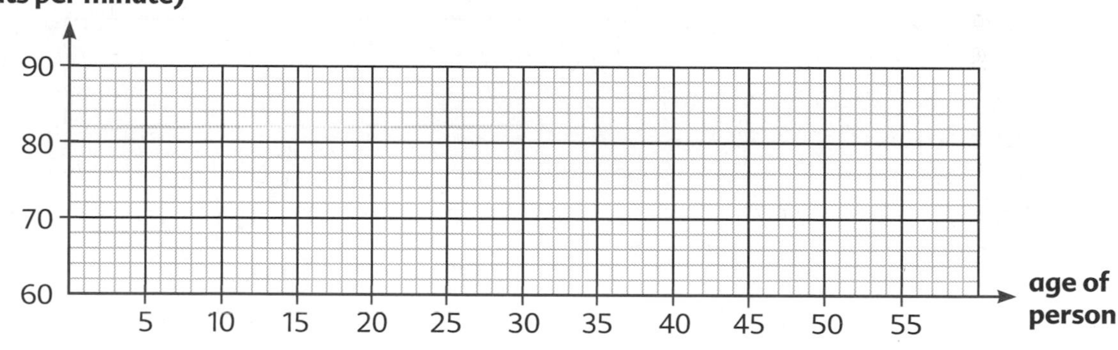

(b) Estimate the heart rate of a 50 year old person. ____________

Name: ______________________ Class: __________ Date: __________

Activity 3.3 The ups and downs of life

Process skills

Observing : the effect of exercise on the heart rate
Inferring : the relationship between exercise and heart rate

Aim: To observe how exercise affects the heart rate of a person

The graph below shows the changes in the heart rate of a boy. He ran on the spot and stopped after some time. Use the readings on the graph below to answer the following questions.

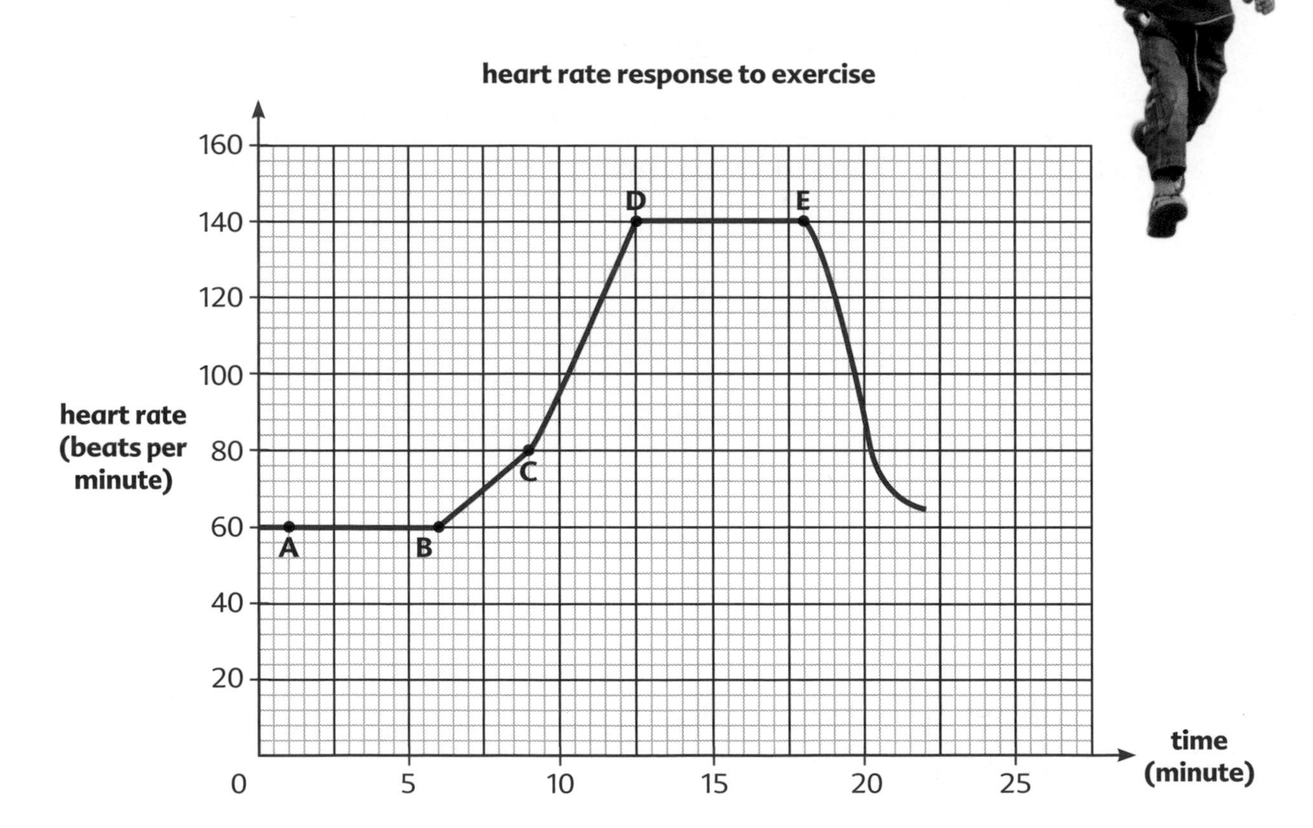

Questions

1. What is the approximate heart rate when the boy is resting?

____

2. At which point (A, B, C, D or E) did he start running?

____

3. At which point (A, B, C, D or E) did he stop running?

____

4. How long did he run?

   Time taken to run = ____________________________

5. What is the difference between his heart rate when he is running and when he is resting?

   Difference = ____________________________

6. (a) What happens to the boy's heart rate when he exercises?

   ____

   (b) Why do you think this happens?

   ____

   ____

   ____

Conclusion

Complete the following sentences by choosing the correct words.

Exercise ________________ (increases/decreases) the heart rate. The heart needs to ________________ (produce/pump) more blood and ________________ (carbon dioxide/oxygen) to various parts of the body to produce more ________________ (energy/sugar).

Reinforcement

Use the given words to complete the concept map.

Blood vessels	Exercise	Fist	Lungs
All the time	Blood	Body	Muscles

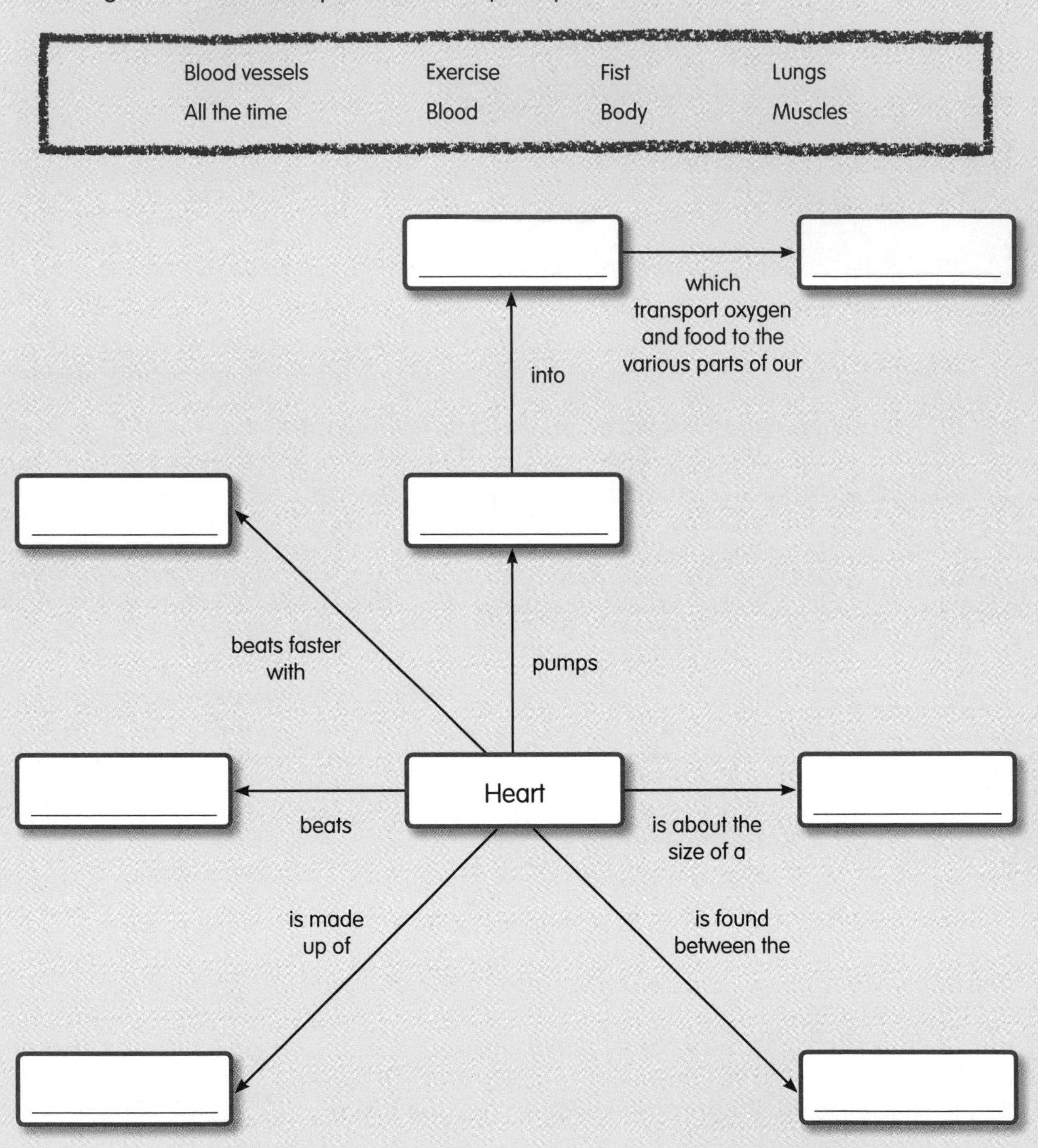

Name: ______________________ Class: __________ Date: __________

Activity 4.1 Micro-organisms in pond water

Process skill

Inferring : how different pond organisms obtain nutrients

Aim: To observe pond micro-organisms using a microscope

Materials: Prepared slides, microscope

When using the microscope to observe things, always use the low power objective first. Change to the high power objective if you need to see more details.

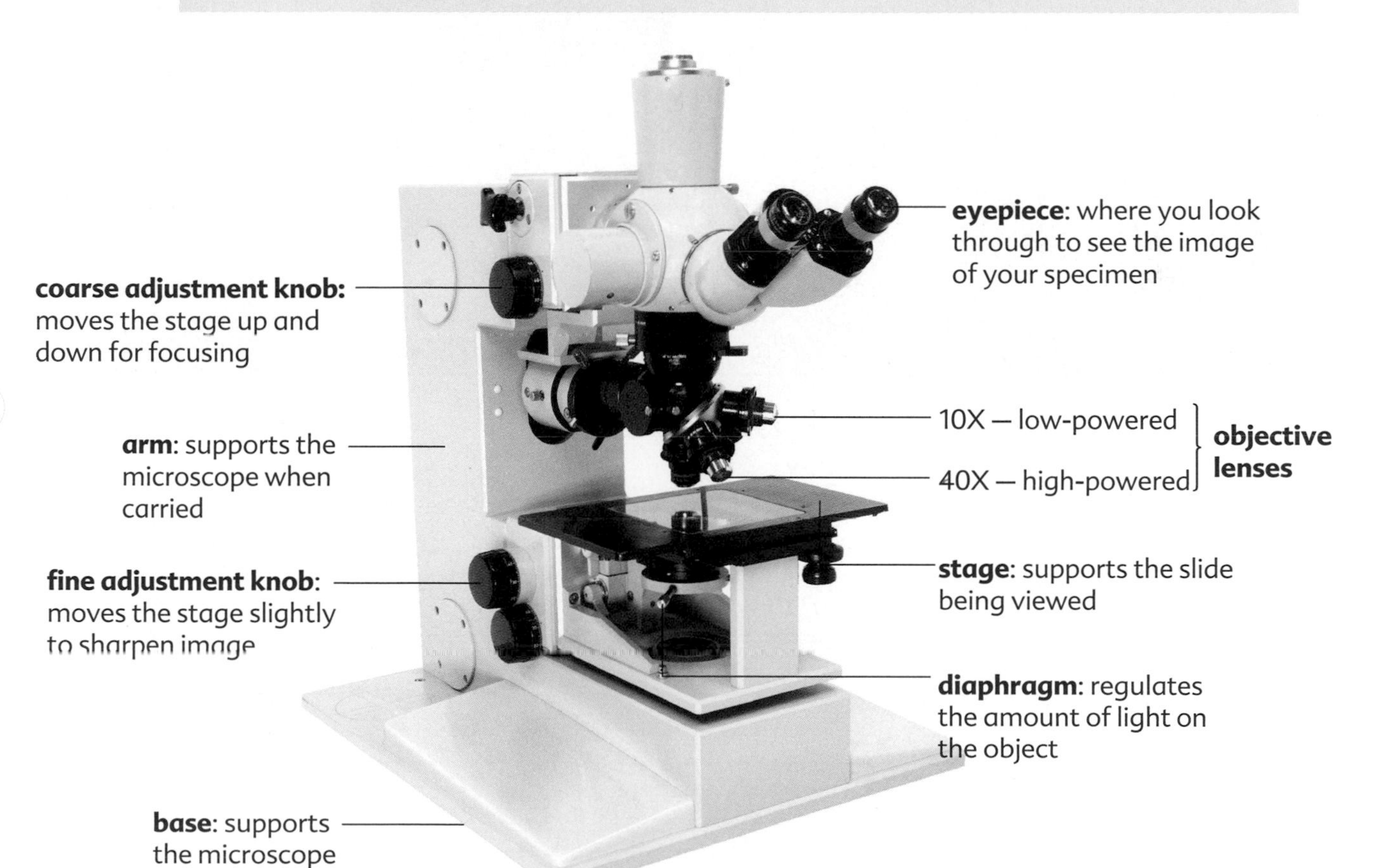

a microscope

Procedures

1. Place a prepared slide on the stage of the microscope.
2. Using the microscope, examine the organisms in the pond water.
3. Repeat steps 1 to 3 if necessary.

Observations

The pictures below show some micro-organisms that may be found in pond water. Put a tick in the box next to the micro-organism if you spot it on your slide.

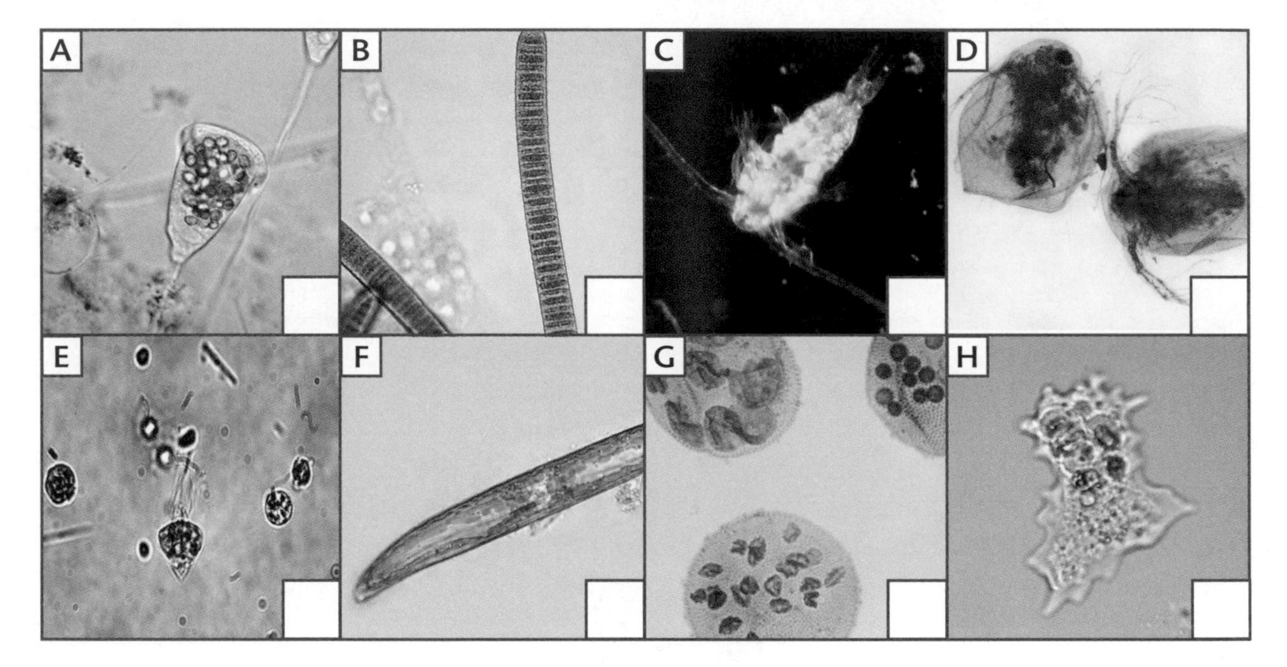

Questions

1. Which of the micro-organisms, A to H, carry out photosynthesis? State the reason for your answer.

____

____

2. The micro-organisms in a pond need ______________, ______________ and ______________ to survive.

3. What are some of the other ways that pond micro-organisms obtain their nutrients besides photosynthesis?

____

____

Planktons are micro-organisms that drift in oceans, seas, lakes or rivers. They are an important source of food to aquatic life. Three groups of planktons are plant planktons, animal planktons and bacteria planktons. Only plant and animal planktons are shown below.

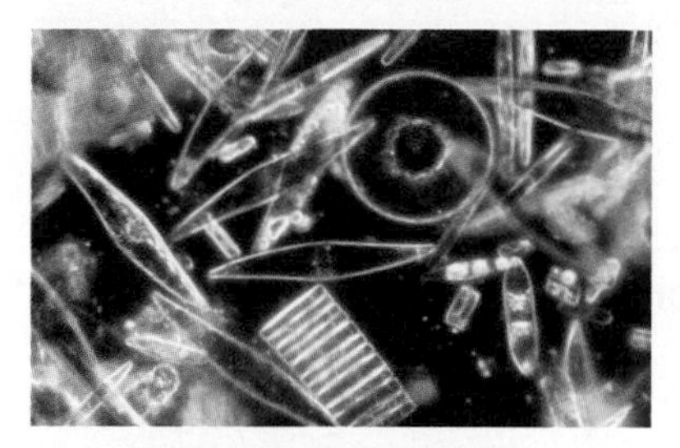

plant planktons

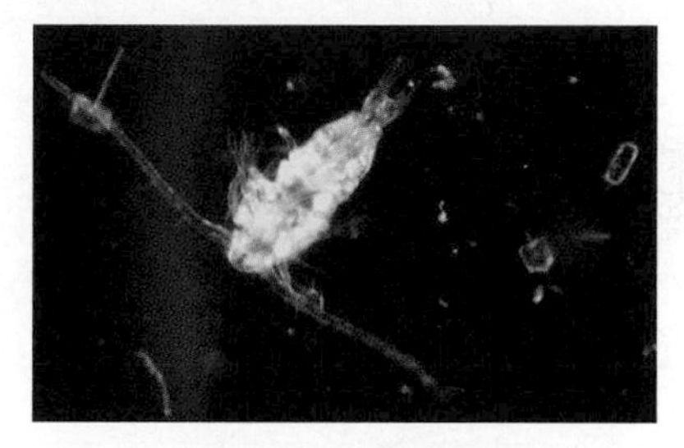

animal plankton

(a) What instrument is needed to observe planktons? ______________

(b) (i) Which group of planktons should contain chloroplast in their cells? ______________

(ii) This group of planktons lives near the water surface. Why are they not found in deep oceans?

____

(c) The oxygen that we breathe not only comes from land plants. It also comes from plant planktons.

Through what process do plant planktons produce oxygen? ______________

Name: ______________________ Class: __________ Date: __________

Activity 4.2 Plant and animal cells

Process skills

Observing : the structures of plant and animal cells
Comparing : the similarities and differences between a plant and animal cell

Aim: To observe plant and animal cells using a microscope

Materials: Toothpick, glass slides, iodine solution, cover slip, a pair of forceps, Elodea plant, microscope, glass dropper

Procedures

1. Use the lens with magnification '10X' written on it. Ensure that the lens has clicked into position.
2. Turn on the light and look down the tube.
3. Place the glass slide on the stage and make sure that the slide is held firmly by the stage clips.
4. Using the coarse adjustment, focus the lens until the image is clear.
5. Rotate the objective lenses of the microscope until the lens with magnification '40X' clicks into position.
6. Using the fine adjustment knob, slowly turn the knob until the image is in focus.

Animal cell

7. Gently scrape the inside of your cheek using the rounded end of a toothpick.
8. Spread the scrapings onto the centre of a clean glass slide and add a small drop of iodine solution to the scrapings.

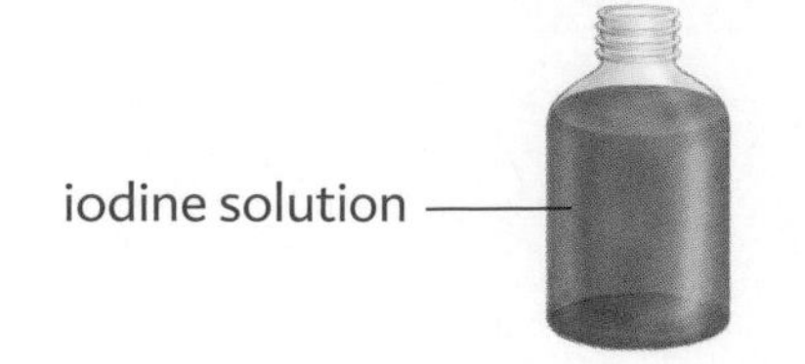

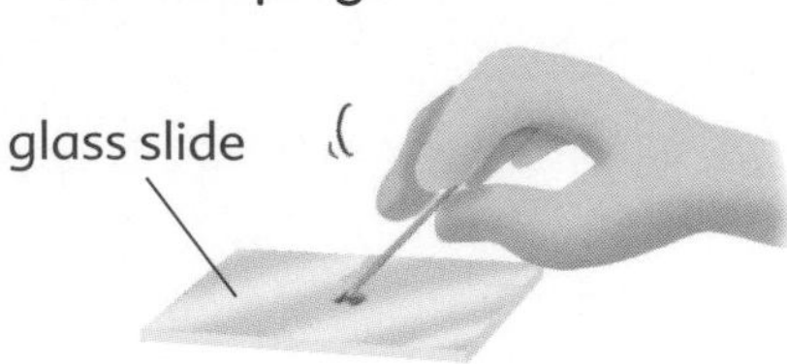

9. Place the cover slip on the glass slide.

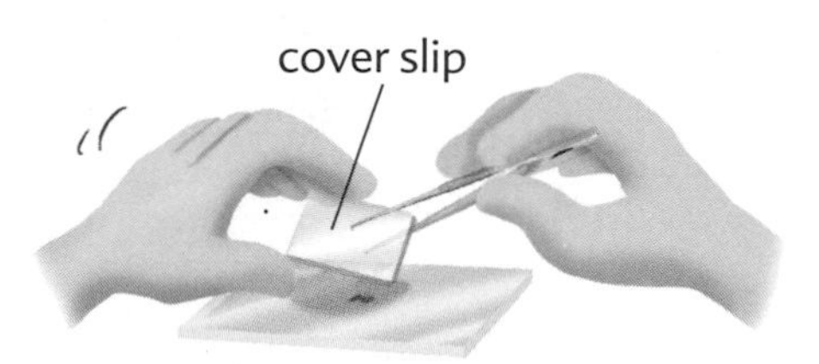

10. Examine the cheek cells under a microscope. Use the low-power objective lens first and then the high-power objective lens.

11. Make drawings of your observations below. Label the parts of the cell.

Plant cell

12. Using a pair of forceps, place an Elodea leaf onto the centre of a clean glass slide.

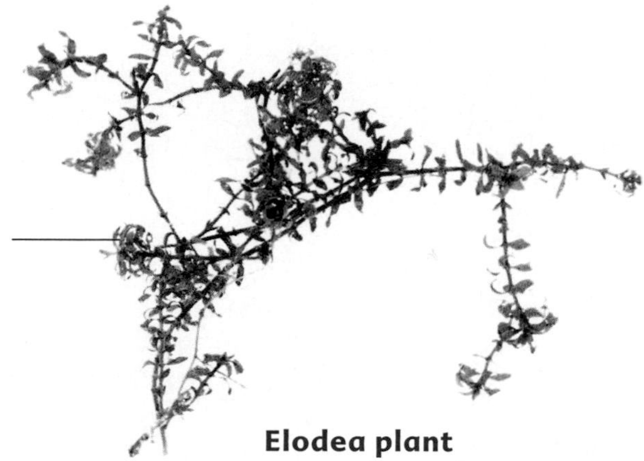

Elodea plant

13. Add a drop of water to the leaf.

14. Repeat steps 9 to 11 as you did for your cheek cells.

Observations

Questions

1. What are the similarities between a plant and an animal cell?

____

2. What are the differences between a plant and an animal cell?

____

Reinforcement

Compare plant and animal cells.

Part of a cell	Animal cell	Plant cell
Cytoplasm		Present
Cell Membrane	Present	
Nucleus	Present	
Cell wall		Present
Chloroplast		Present

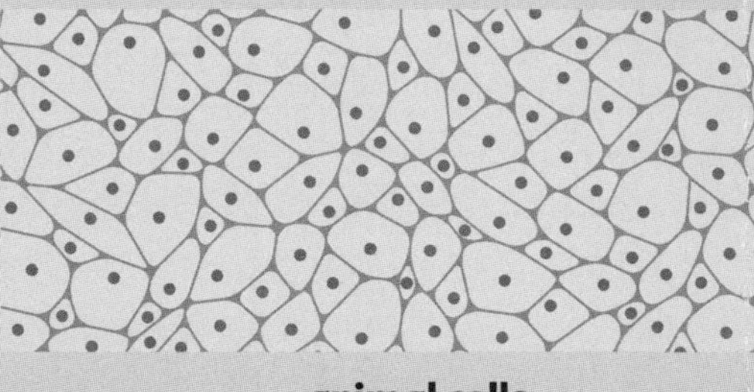

animal cells

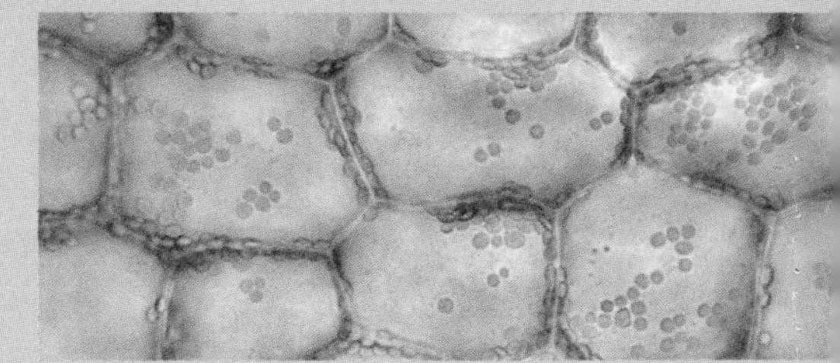

plant cells

Extension

In this activity, you have observed a typical animal cell and a typical plant cell.

In comparison to the plant cell, would you expect to see the same structures if you were to observe the cells of an onion scale leaf? How will they differ? (Hint: The Elodea leaf makes food for the Elodea plant but the onion scale leaf does not make food for the onion plant.)

____

____

____

Name: ______________________________ Class: ________ Date: ________

Activity 4.3 Leaf prints

Process skill

Communicating : observations and conclusions

Aim: To relate the structure of a cell to its function

Materials: Microscope, glass slide, cover slip, nail polish, leaf, a pair of forceps

Procedures

1. Apply nail polish over one part of the underside of the leaf. Allow the nail polish to dry.

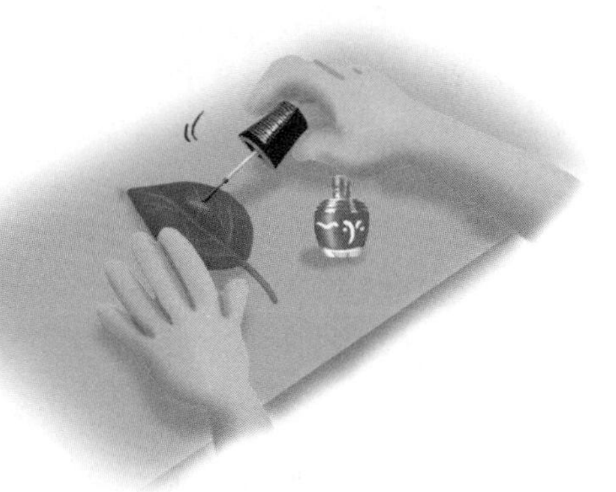

Do not breathe in the nail polish vapour.

2. Using a pair of forceps, carefully peel the layer of dried nail polish off the leaf (the 'peel').

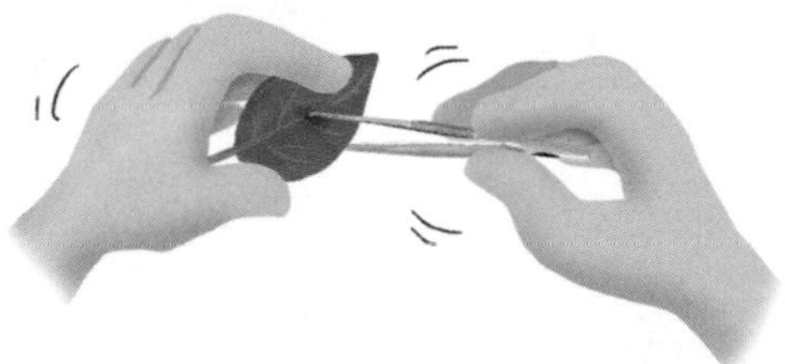

3. Place the 'peel' on a clean glass slide and place a cover slip over the 'peel'.

4. Observe the 'peel' under a microscope. Use the low-power objective lens first and then the high-power objective lens.

The diagram below is a picture of the 'peel' you may have observed under the microscope.

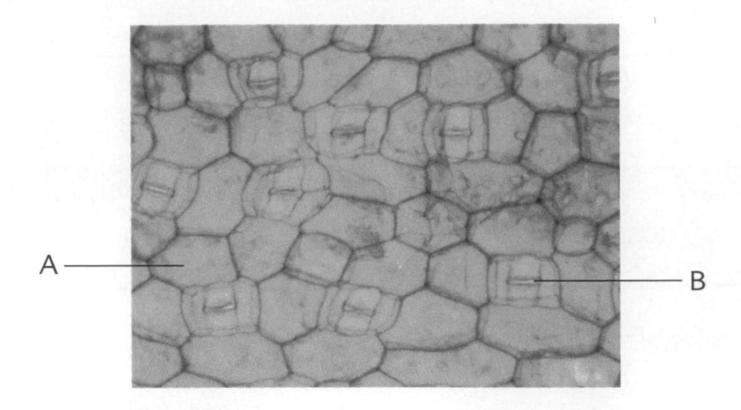

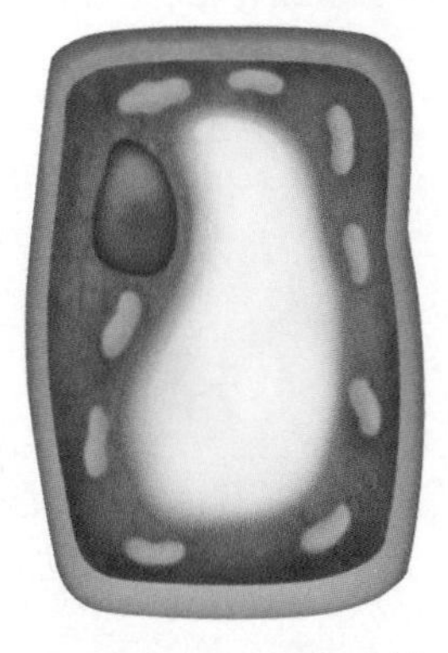

A: epidermal cell

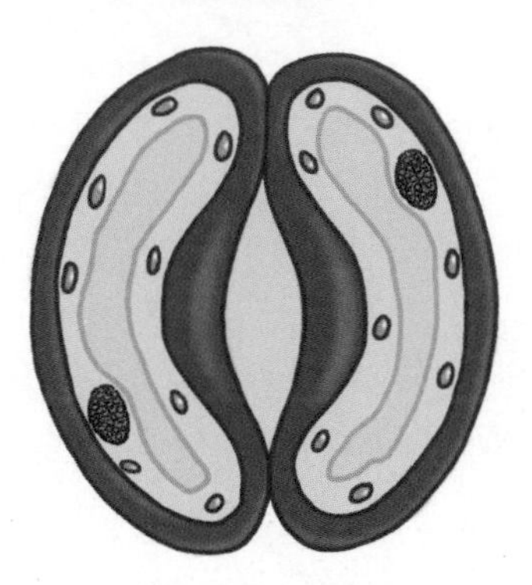

B: guard cell

Conclusion

What can you conclude about the 'peel' you made?

Extension

Observe the following diagram of guard cells found in plants and answer the questions on the following page.

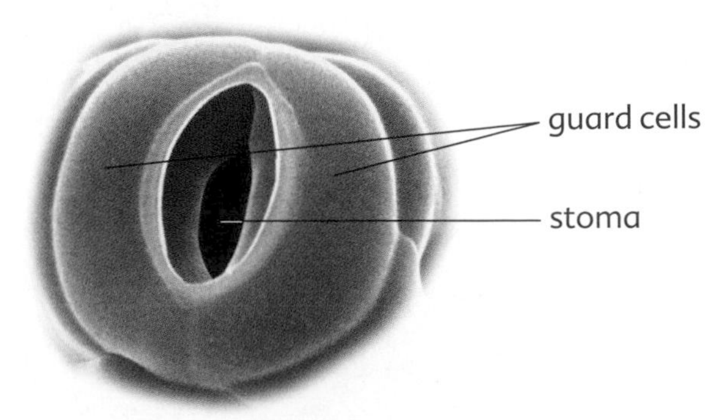

1. Why do you think guard cells are called as such?

2. Predict whether you will observe the same picture when the upper surface of the leaf is used to make the 'peel'. Explain your answer. (Hint: Having too many stomata can increase water loss.)

3. What would you do to confirm your prediction?

Reinforcement

A cell is made up of different parts which have different functions. Some parts are found in both the animal and plant cells. Some can only be found in plant cells. Complete the table below.

	Part of cell	Function of cell	Is this part found in both animal and plant cells?
(a)		Gives shape to the cell	No. It is not found in an animal cell. It is only found in a plant cell.
(b)		Controls movement of substances in and out of the cell	
(c)	Nucleus		Yes, it is found in both animal and plant cells.
(d)	Cytoplasm		
(e)		Traps light energy for photosynthesis	

Name: ______________________ Class: ________ Date: ________

Activity 4.4 My cell model

Process skills

Applying : knowledge of cells to build a cell model
Communicating : ideas on the structure of a cell using a model

Aim: To make a 3D model of a cell

Materials: Resealable plastic bags, honey or syrup, assortment of edible objects to represent the parts of the cell, (e.g., chocolate balls and jelly beans)

Procedures

1. Work in groups of three. Discuss and decide whether to make a plant or animal cell.

2. Create a cell model using the materials mentioned above.

3. Draw and colour a picture of the model you created and paste it in the space provided below. Alternatively, you may take a picture of your model using a digital camera and print it out. Name the parts of the cell in the picture.

Name: ______________________ Class: ________ Date: ________

Activity 5.1 Electrical components

Process skills

Identifying : parts of electrical components
Constructing : simple circuits

Aim: To identify different electrical components and to connect the electrical components together to light up a bulb

Materials: A battery (D-sized), a piece of wire, a bulb, a magnifying glass

Procedures

1. Look at the battery provided.

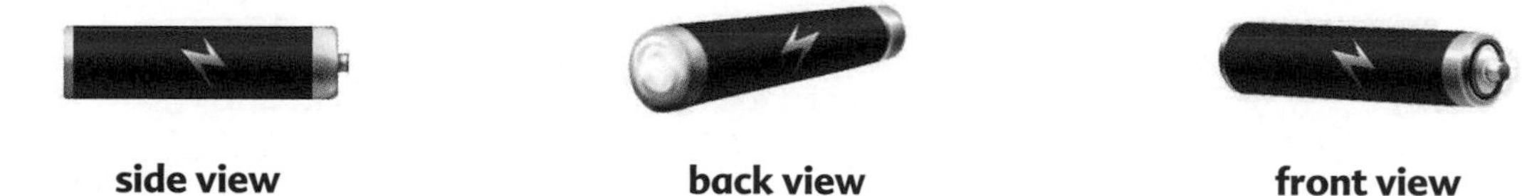

side view **back view** **front view**

   (a) On the side-view diagram above, write a '+' and '–' to show the different terminals of a battery.

   (b) Look for the parts of the battery made of metal. Shade them with your pencil in the back-view and front-view diagrams.

2. Look at the wire given to you. Draw the wire and label the part made of metal and the part made of plastic or rubber.

3. Look at the bulb using a magnifying glass. Refer to your textbook and identify the various parts of the bulb. Label them in the diagram below.

4. Try the different ways of connecting the components to light up the bulb. Put a tick in the box if it lights up.

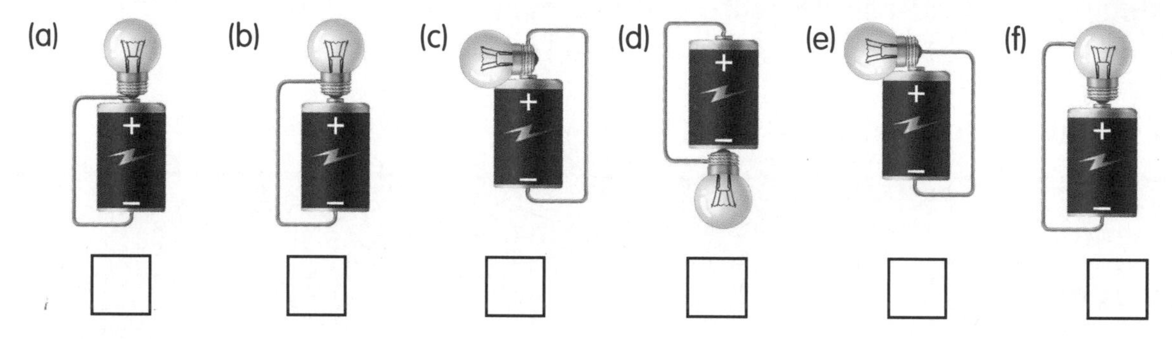

Questions

1. Why must a battery always be present in a circuit, for the bulb to light up?

____

____

2. How must a bulb be connected in a circuit?

____

Reinforcement

Fill in the boxes with the correct component.

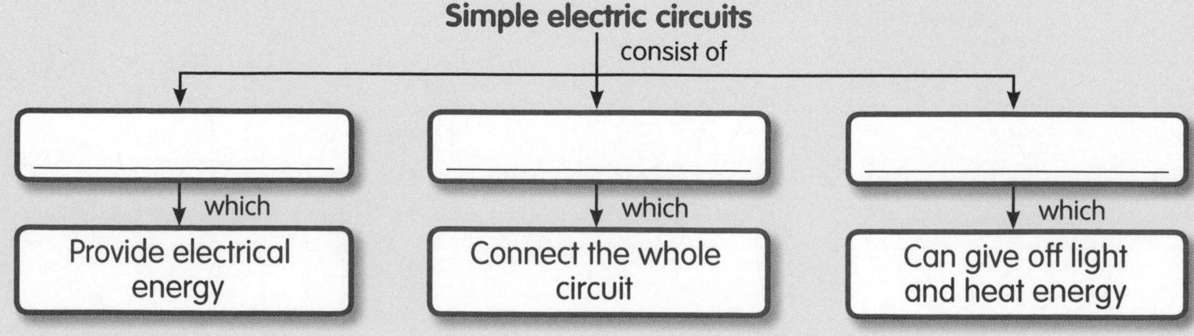

Name: ______________________ Class: __________ Date: __________

Activity 5.2 Closed circuits

Process skills

Analysing : a closed circuit
Predicting : if a bulb will light up

Aim: To find out if a bulb in a circuit will light up

Materials: A battery (D-sized), three pieces of wires, three pieces of wires with crocodile clips at the ends, a bulb, a piece of stiff cardboard, six steel paper clips, masking tape

Procedures

1. Construct a simple circuit as shown below. Tape the wires to the battery and the bulb.

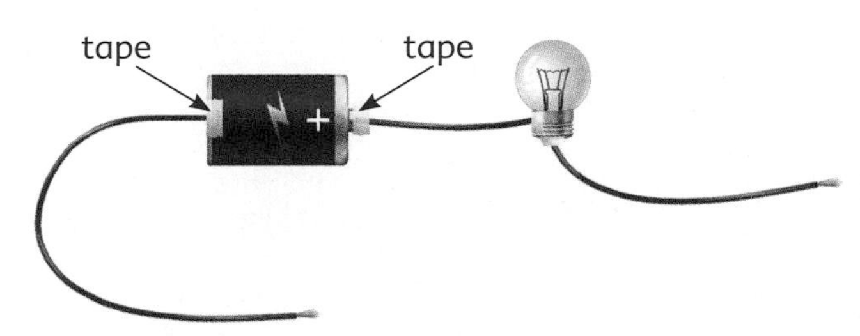

2. (a) Clip the six steel paper clips onto the cardboard as shown below. Label the paper clips A to F.

   (b) Join some of the paper clips using pieces of wires with crocodile clips at the ends. An example is shown below.

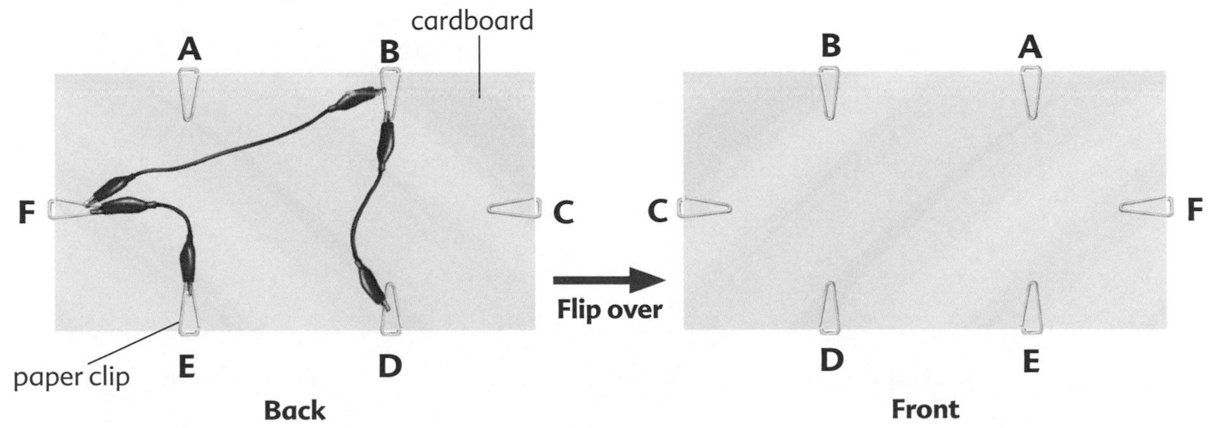

3. Flip the cardboard over so that your friend cannot see the connections you have made. Then get your friend to use the simple circuit to guess how the connections are made below the cardboard.

Guess how these paper clips are connected.

Question

Get your friend to draw what he or she thinks is the connection you have made below your cardboard.

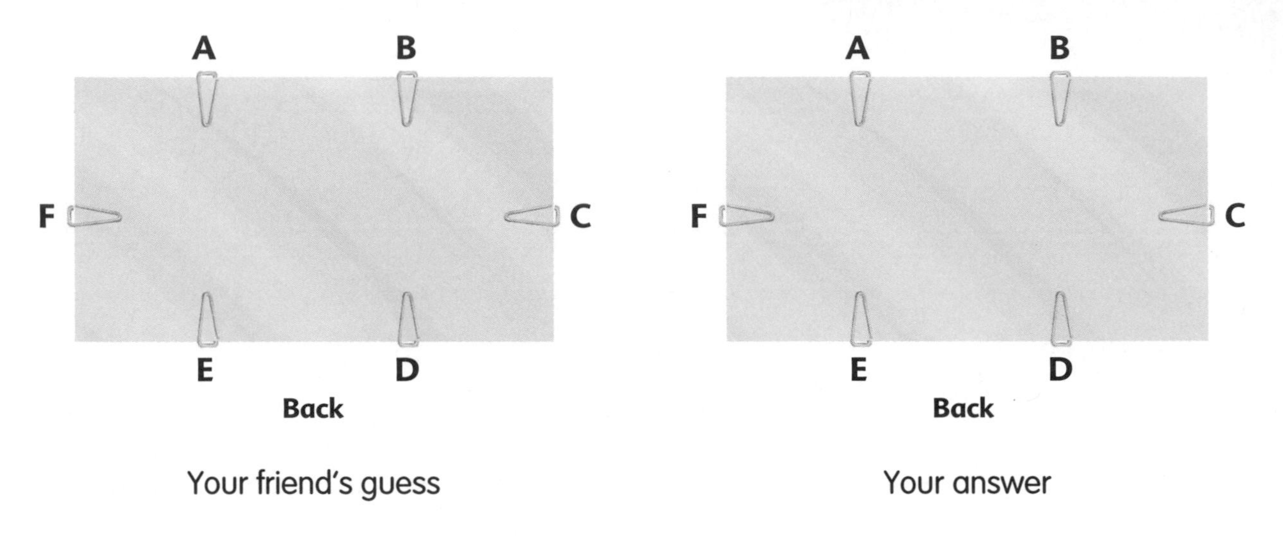

Your friend's guess

Your answer

Is your friend correct? ____________________

Extension

Here is a card with some questions. Draw lines to show how the paper clips should be connected.

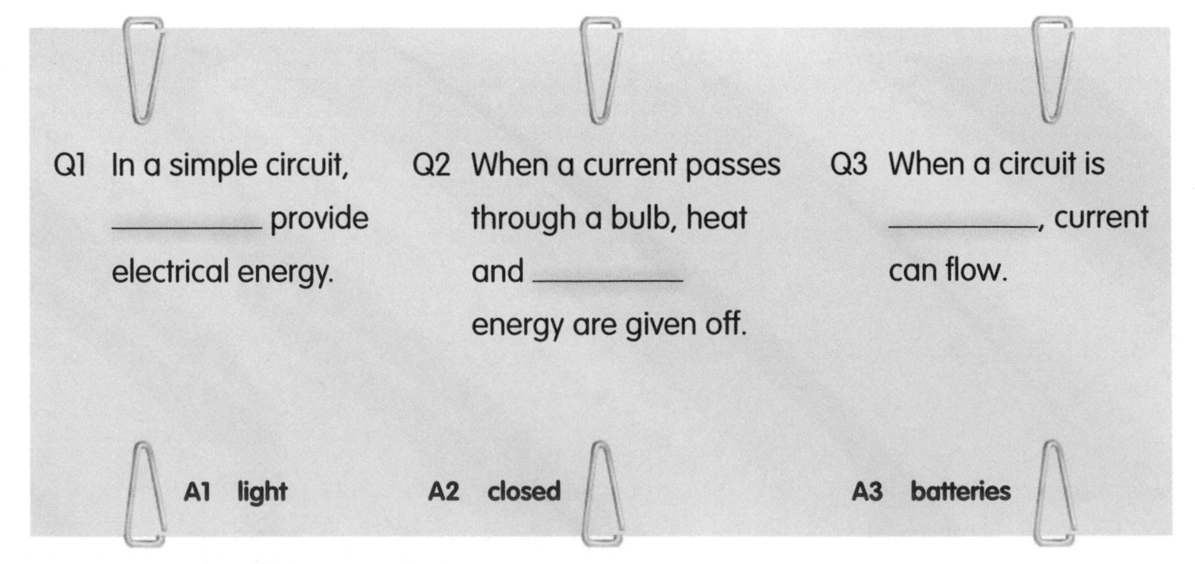

Name: ______________________ Class: __________ Date: __________

Activity 6.1 More batteries in series

Process skills

Constructing : simple circuits from diagrams of circuits
Investigating : the effect of the number of batteries (arranged in series) on the current in a circuit
Communicating : circuit diagrams from diagrams of circuits

Aim: To find out the effect of connecting more batteries in series to a bulb

Materials: Four batteries (D-sized, each in a battery holder), a bulb in a bulb holder, some connecting wires, magnifying glass

Procedures

1. Will connecting more batteries in series to a bulb make the bulb brighter? Write down your prediction.

   ____

   ____

   Refer to the circuits below as you follow the steps.

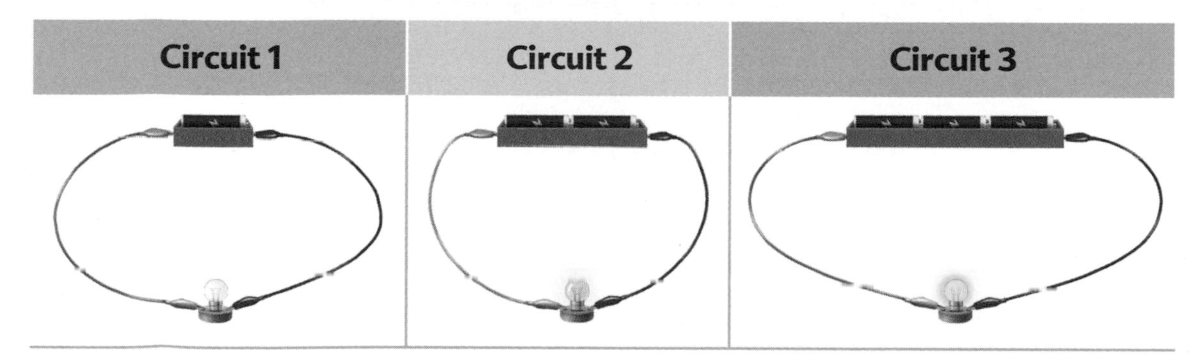

2. Construct circuit 1 and observe the brightness of the bulb.

3. Connect one more battery in series to circuit 1. The circuit now looks like circuit 2. Observe the brightness of the bulb.

Do not touch the bulb as it may be very hot during the experiment.

4. Connect one more battery in series to circuit 2. The circuit now looks like circuit 3. Observe the brightness of the bulb.

5. **(Optional)** Connect one more battery in series to circuit 3 until the bulb blows. Use a magnifying glass to observe the filament of the blown bulb.

Observations

1. Fill in the table with the number that represents the circuits on the previous page.

Brightness of bulb	Circuit
Bright	
Brighter	
Brightest	

2. **(Optional)** What happened to the metal filament when the bulb blew?

____

Questions

1. The number of batteries in circuit 2 is reduced by one. When the circuit is reconnected to form circuit 1, the electric | | | r | | e | | t | flowing in the circuit ______________. The bulb becomes ______________.

2. Draw the circuit diagrams for circuits 1, 2 and 3.

circuit 1

circuit 2

circuit 3

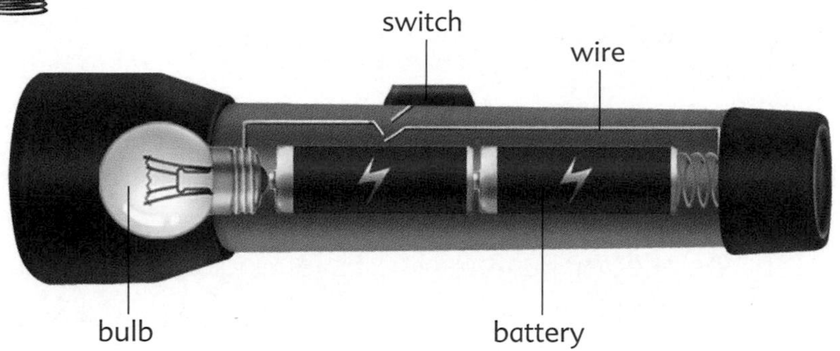

1. Are the batteries in a torch connected in series or in parallel to the bulb? How can you tell?

____

____

2. Draw a circuit diagram to represent the circuit of the torch.

Name: ______________________ Class: __________ Date: __________

Activity 6.2 More bulbs in series

Process skills

Constructing : simple circuits from diagrams of circuits
Investigating : the effect of number of bulbs (arranged in series) on the current in a circuit
Communicating : using circuit diagrams

Aim: To find out the effect of connecting more bulbs to a circuit

Materials: Three batteries (D-sized, each in a battery holder), three bulbs (each in a bulb holder), some wires

Procedures

1. Will connecting more bulbs in series make the bulbs dimmer? Write down your prediction.

   ____

   Refer to the circuits below as you follow the steps.

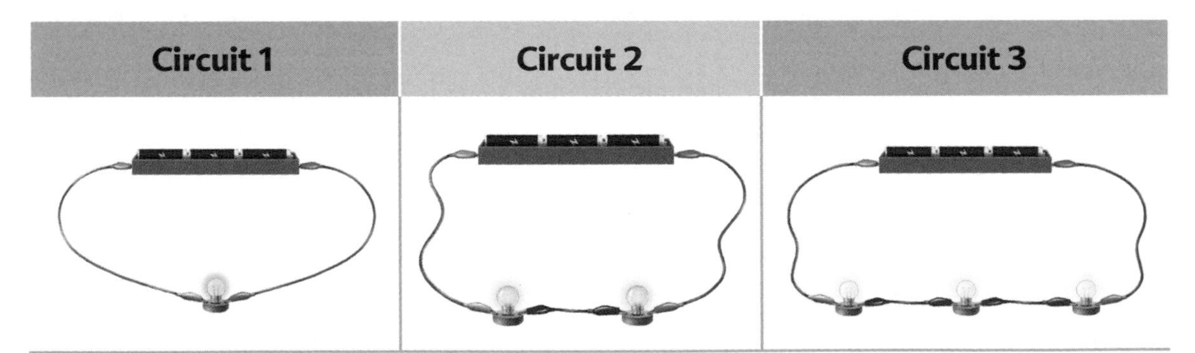

2. Construct circuit 1 and observe the brightness of the bulb.

3. Connect one more bulb in series to circuit 1. The circuit now looks like circuit 2. Observe the brightness of the bulbs.

4. Connect one more bulb in series to circuit 2. The circuit now looks like circuit 3. Observe the brightness of the bulbs.

Observations

Fill in the blank spaces in the table with the number that represents the circuit.

Brightness of bulb	Circuit
Bright	
Brighter	
Brightest	

Questions

1. The number of bulbs in circuit 3 is reduced by one. When the circuit is reconnected to form circuit 2, the electric [ ][ ][r][ ][e][ ][t] flowing in the circuit ________________ (increases/decreases) as it is easier for it to flow. The bulb will become________________ (dimmer/brighter).

2. Do you think the bulbs will continue to light up if more and more bulbs are connected in series to the circuit? What makes you think so?

____

____

____

3. Draw the circuit diagrams for circuits 1, 2 and 3.

circuit 1

circuit 2

circuit 3

Name: ______________________ Class: __________ Date: __________

Activity 6.3 Bulbs, re-arrange!

Process skills

Constructing : simple circuits from diagrams of circuits
Investigating : the effect of the arrangement of bulbs on the current in a circuit

Aim: To find out how brightly bulbs will shine, when bulbs are arranged in series and in parallel

Materials: One battery (D-sized, in a battery holder), two bulbs (each in a bulb holder), some connecting wires

Procedures

1. Will connecting bulbs in parallel make the bulbs dimmer or brighter? Write down your prediction.

   ____

   Refer to the circuits below as you follow the steps.

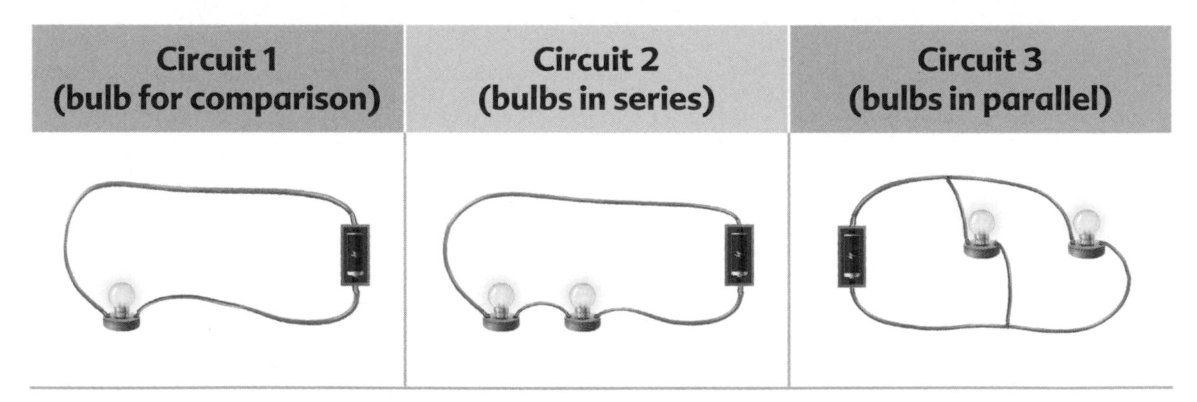

2. Construct circuit 1 and observe the brightness of the bulb.

3. Connect one more bulb in series to circuit 1. The circuit now looks like circuit 2. Observe the brightness of the bulbs.

4. Remove one of the bulbs from circuit 2 and connect it in parallel as shown in circuit 3. Observe the brightness of the bulbs.

Observations

1. The bulbs in circuits __________ and __________ light up as brightly as each other.
2. The bulbs in circuit __________ light up less brightly than the bulbs in circuits __________ and __________.

Questions

1. How should two bulbs in a circuit be arranged to produce the brightest light?

   ____

2. Draw the circuit diagrams of circuits 1, 2 and 3 in the space below.

circuit 1 (bulb for comparison)	**circuit 2 (bulbs in series)**	**circuit 3 (bulbs in parallel)**

Conclusion

What is the effect of changing the arrangement of bulbs in a circuit?

____

____

1. (a) Predict the degree of brightness of the bulbs in the following circuits. Rank them in order, from brightest to least bright. ____________________

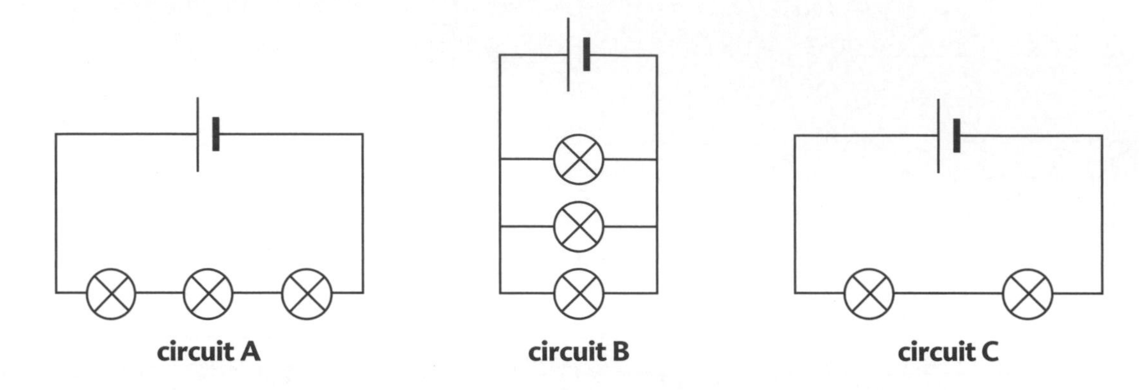

(b) Complete the following table by stating whether the remaining bulbs in each circuit will continue to light up if one of the bulbs is blown.

Circuit A	Circuit B	Circuit C

2. (a) Do you think the lamps in a house are arranged in series or parallel?

____

____

(b) What is the advantage of using this arrangement for the lamps in the house?

____

____

Name: ______________________ Class: ________ Date: ________

Activity 7.1 Conductors and insulators

Process skills

Constructing : simple circuits from circuit diagrams
Classifying : electrical conductors and insulators

Aim: To find out what materials allow electricity to pass through

Materials: Two batteries (D-sized, each in a battery holder), a bulb in a bulb holder, some wires, common objects in the classroom

Background information

If the bulb lights up, the object allows electricity to pass through. Objects that allow electricity to pass through are called conductors of electricity. If the bulb does not light up, the object does not allow electricity to pass through. Objects that do not allow electricity to pass through are called insulators of electricity.

Procedures

1. Construct a circuit tester as shown below.

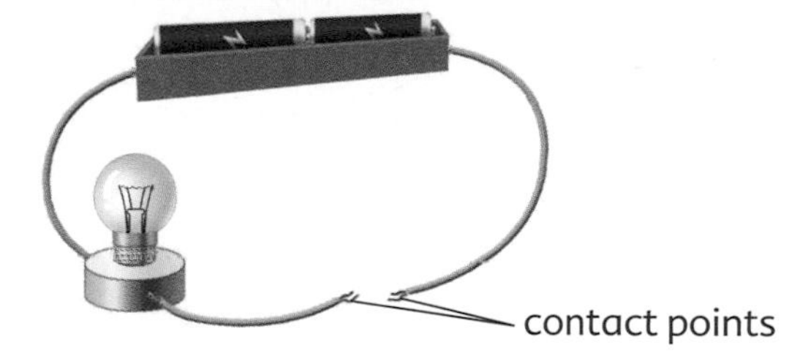

Do not touch the contact points with your bare hands.

2. Use the contact points to touch some objects in the classroom and observe if the bulb lights up. Choose some objects that will make the bulb light up and some that will not make the bulb light up.

Observations

Complete the table below.

Object	Material tested	Did the bulb light up?
Pencil	Wood	No

Question

Classify the materials tested using the following graphic organiser.

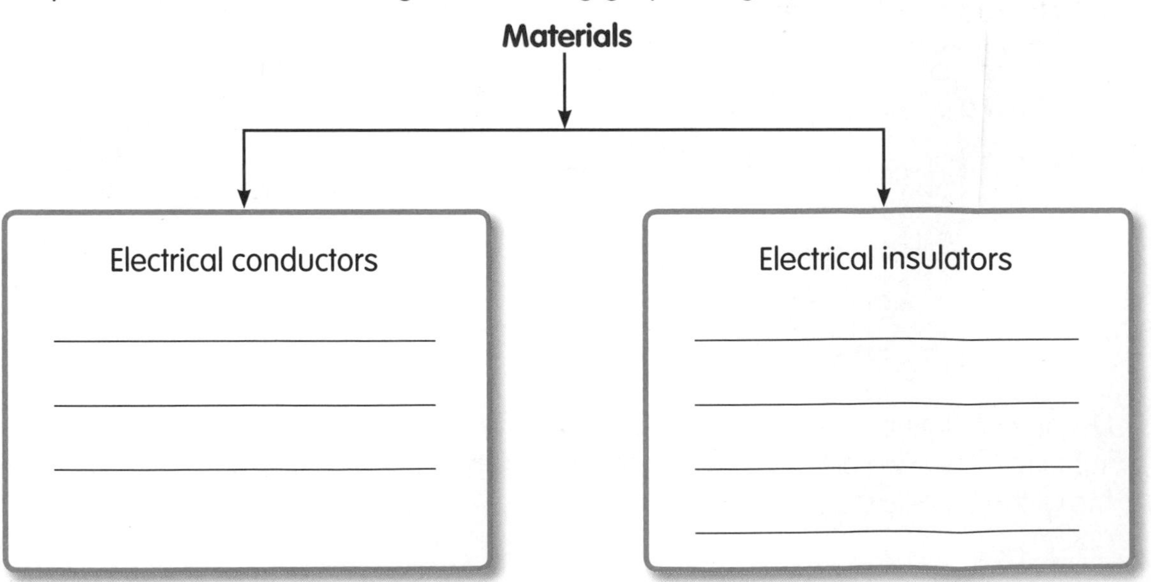

Reinforcement

Fill in the blanks with the correct answers.

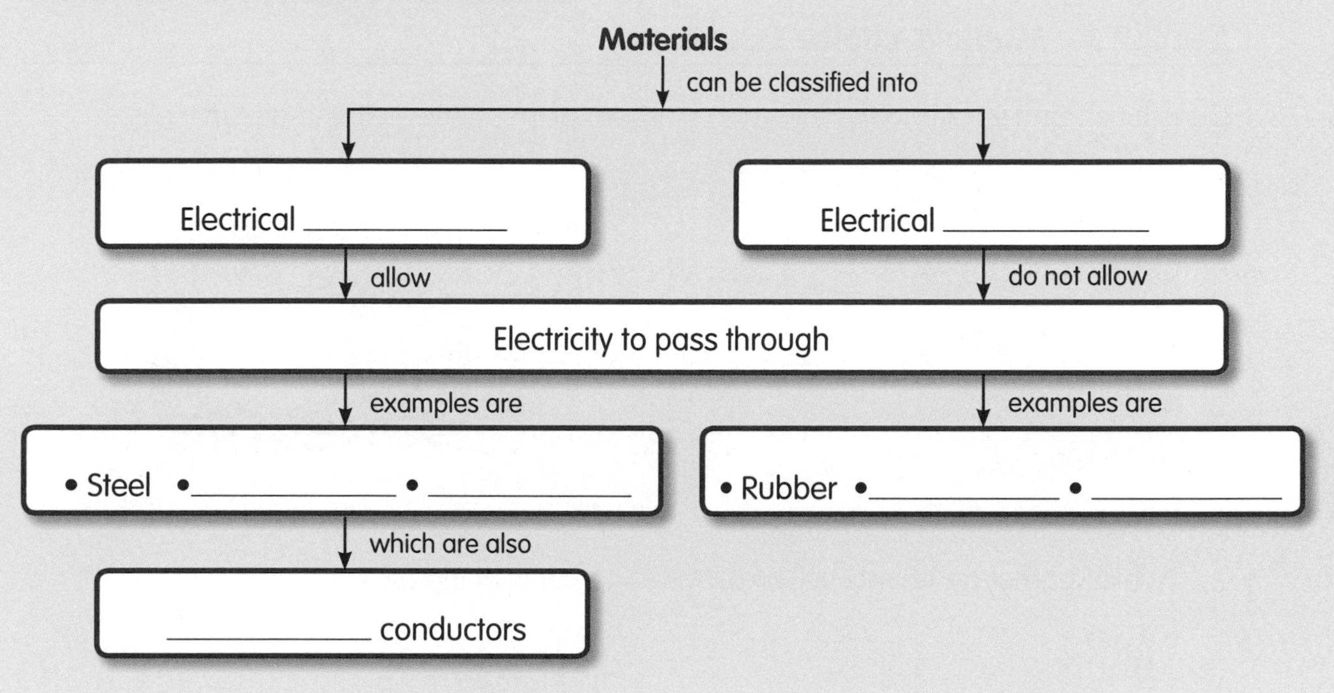

Extension

Classify the labelled parts into good conductors and insulators of electricity.

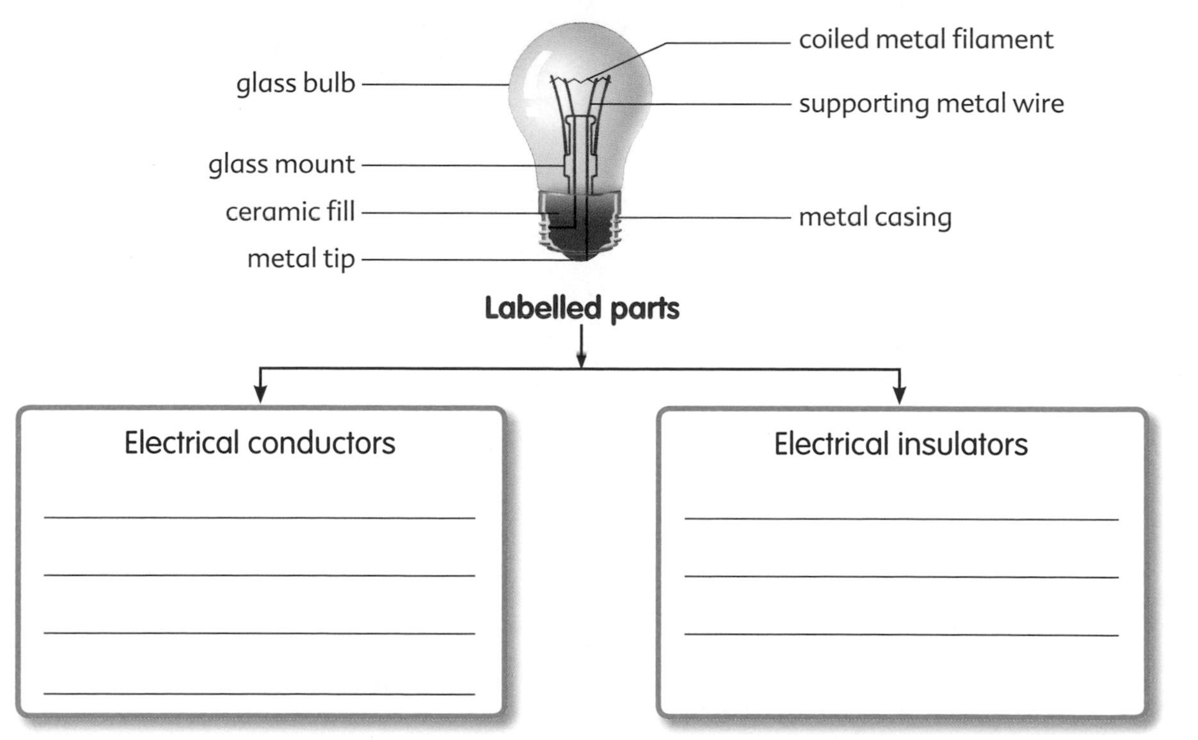

Name: ______________________ Class: __________ Date: __________

Revision Exercise Systems

Section A : Multiple-choice Questions

Questions 1 and 2 refer to the following diagram of an animal cell and a plant cell.

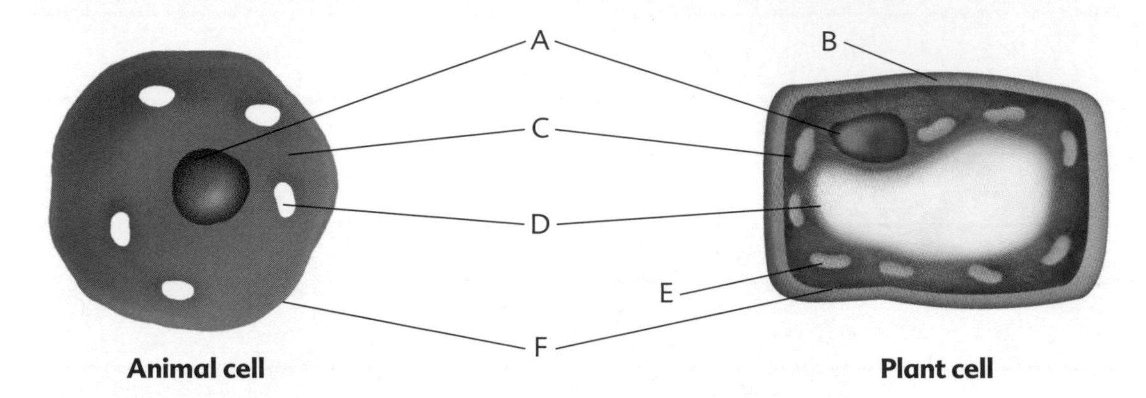

1. Which part of an animal cell protects the contents of the cell?

   (1) A (2) B
   (3) C (4) F ( )

2. Which of the following controls all the activities in the cell?

   (1) A (2) B
   (3) C (4) D ( )

3. Study the following circuit.

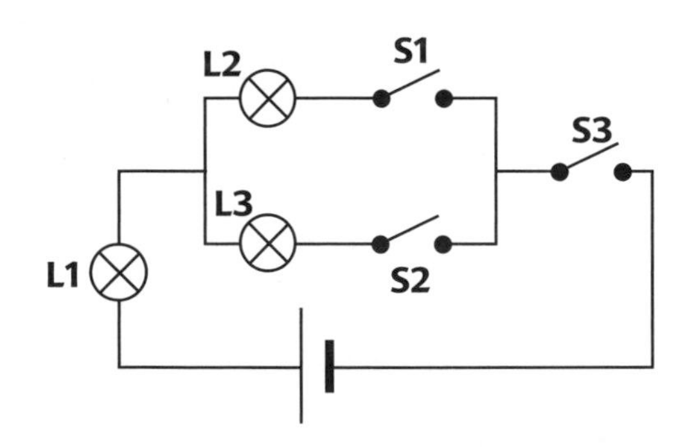

Which switches should be closed to light up only lamps L1 and L3?

(1) S1 and S2 only
(2) S1 and S3 only
(3) S2 and S3 only
(4) S1, S2 and S3 ( )

4. Rubber is an electrical insulator because ________.
   (1) it is not a source of light
   (2) it is not a source of heat
   (3) it does not allow heat to pass through
   (4) it does not allow electricity to pass through ( )

5. In the circuit shown below, the nichrome wire becomes hot when the switch is on.

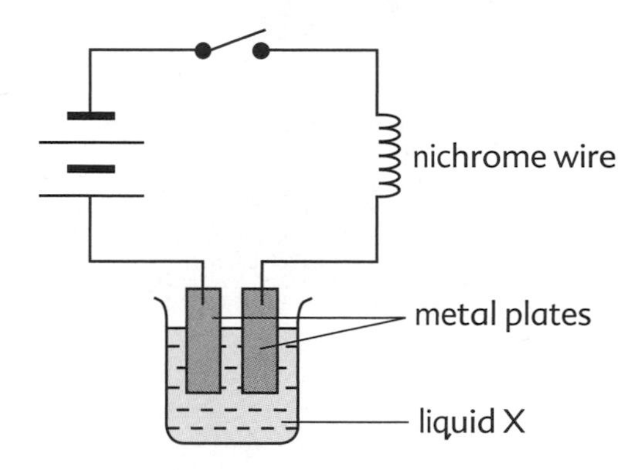

   What conclusion can you draw from the experiment?
   (1) Liquid X is an electrical conductor.
   (2) Liquid X is an electrical insulator.
   (3) Liquid X is a heat conductor.
   (4) Liquid X is a heat insulator. ( )

Section B : Structured Questions

6. Use the given words to complete the diagram that shows how blood flows in certain parts of the body. Some words can be used more than once.

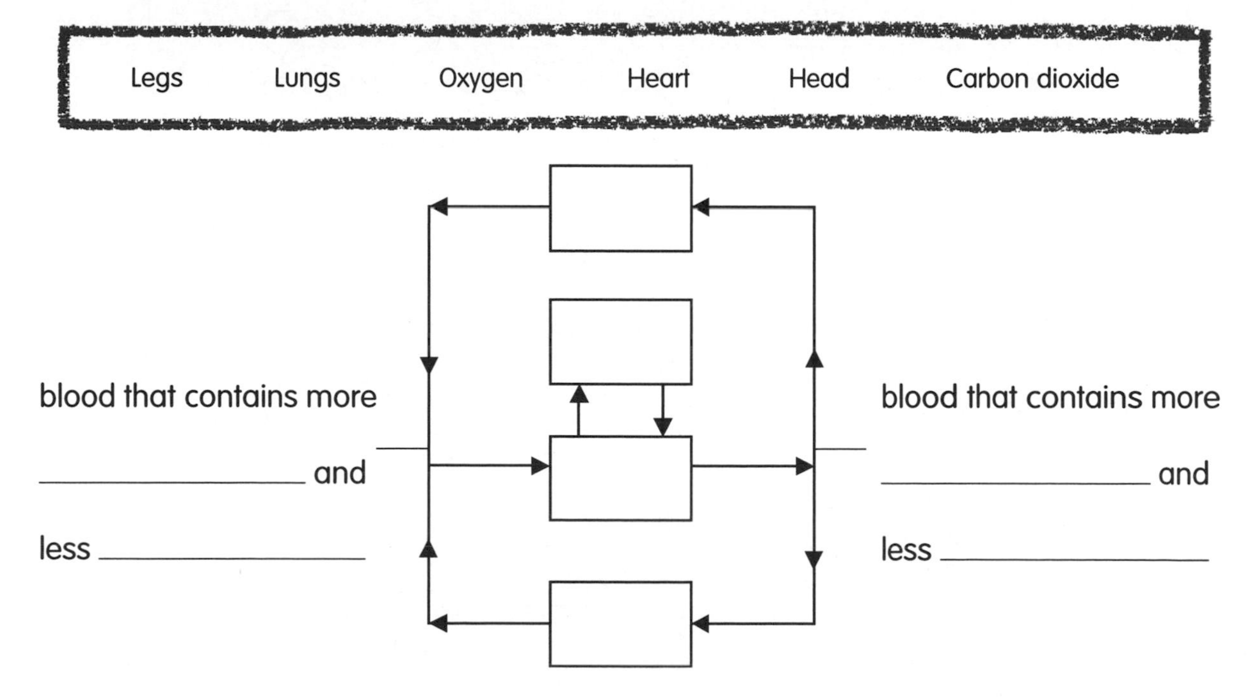

7. An outer ring of a stem was removed from a plant as shown below.

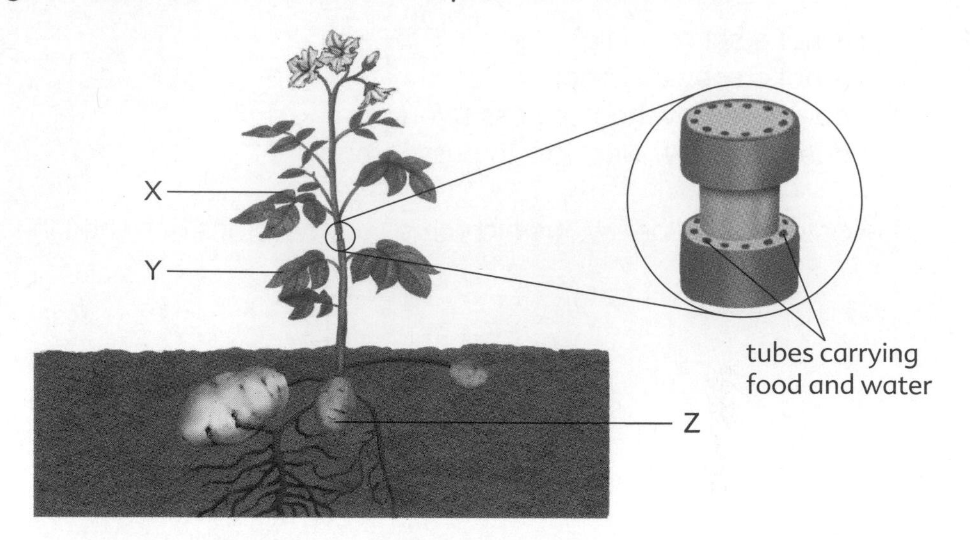

(a) What would happen to X? ______________________________

(b) What would happen to Y? ______________________________

(c) What would happen to Z? ______________________________

8. Study the circuits below. A and B represent different materials.

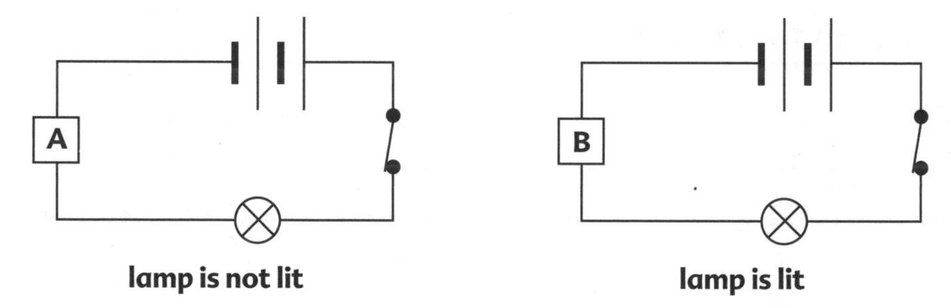

Materials A and B are connected to another circuit as shown below.

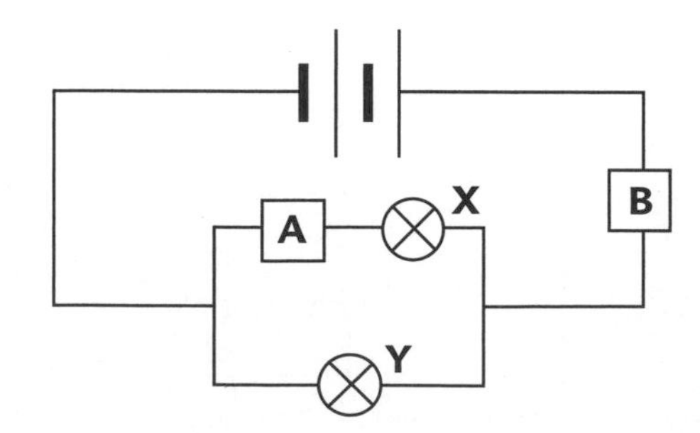

Will the bulbs, X and Y, light up? Explain your answer.

____

____